A PHOTOGRAPHIC
GUIDE TO **Shetland's
Geology**

A PHOTOGRAPHIC
GUIDE TO

Shetland's
Geology

David Malcolm & Robina R. Barton

The Shetland Times Ltd.
Lerwick
2015

A Photographic Guide to Shetland's Geology

ISBN 978-1-904746-97-3

A catalogue record for this book is available from the British Library.

Front cover (main picture): Turbidite, Skaw Beach, Unst.
Back cover (upper): Light colour is quartzite; dark ring is mica and quartz.
Back cover (lower): Banded sandstone, Braewick Beach.

Printed and published by
The Shetland Times Ltd.,
Gremista, Lerwick,
Shetland ZE1 0PX.

Contents

Preface

Over the past few years, a number of illustrated guide books have appeared with respect to Shetland's wild flowers and bird life. To date, nothing specific has been available for the non-specialist with regards to the islands' geology. The authors hope that this work will go some way to filling the gap. Geology is not the remit of an academic few but is something that is available to and can be enjoyed by all. Furthermore, we do not have to venture far afield. For many of us, rich and exciting geological treasures lie right on our doorstep. The purpose of this book is to help you to find and identify those treasures!

The remains of an ancient desert landscape can be seen at the Sands of Sound, a few minute's walk from the Quoys housing estate.

David Malcolm
Robina R. Barton

Acknowledgements

The authors wish to take this opportunity to thank the many friends and colleagues who have given much appreciated support throughout the preparation of this book and to those who have provided many helpful suggestions. In particular, we are grateful to:

Paul Harvey, Shetland Amenity Trust – for his encouragement in converting what was a vision over many years, into the work you hold in your hands today.

Allen Fraser – for sharing his expertise and helping with the identification of many of the rocks illustrated in this book. Also for his helpful guidance and advice about the layout and contents of this work.

Jonathan Swale, Scottish Natural Heritage – for proof reading the entire text, reviewing all the photographs, assisting in writing up the captions and making many helpful suggestions besides.

Eileen Brooke-Freeman, Shetland Amenity Trust – for proof reading all the place names referred to in the text and making recommendations where appropriate.

Sandisons (Unst) – for granting access to the quarry at Clibberswick.

Jonathan Wills – for granting one of us (DM) free passage on MV *Dunter* to access and photograph the magnificent cliffs of Bressay and Noss.

Sheila Fraser – for spotting the fossil fish at Exnaboe on a field studies trip. Thanks Sheila!

Saro Saravanan – for helping one of us (DM) with the computerised aspects of photography and designing the metamorphic rock grade scale.

Scottish Geodiversity Forum for help with the glossary of geological terms.

Walter Scott, Scalloway – for helpful suggestions and numerous corrections to the text (excluding the formatting and spelling of place names) following the publication of the first edition in 2015.

Most of the photographs in this book have been taken by one of us (DM), but the authors wish to thank Dave Donaldson, Billy Fox, Allen Fraser, and Jonathan Swale for filling important gaps and contributing excellent photographs. Where relevant, the photographer's name is inserted alongside their contribution.

Introduction

Shetland's 1420 square km (556 square miles) form a mere 0.6% of the land surface of the United Kingdom, but this archipelago of over 100 islands has a richer, more diverse and dramatic geological heritage than any comparable area in Britain. Indeed, at the time of writing, Shetland is one of only two designated Global Geoparks in Scotland. The rocks of Shetland tell a story of continental collisions, arid deserts, ancient lakes, massive volcanoes, ice, wind and waves.

It is very tempting to believe that geology is a static, inert science but nothing could be further from the truth. Our bird life, wild flowers, human settlements and activity are all intricately bound up with the rocks around us and the soil beneath our feet!

This book is not an exhaustive text of Shetland's geology. Rather, it is a pictorial guide to many of our more commonly occurring rocks, with the inclusion of some rarer examples, plus a few minerals as well.

Geologists classify rocks into three main types: igneous, metamorphic and sedimentary. With this in mind the rocks in this book have been grouped into sections based on these major rock types. The rocks on the east side of Unst and part of Fetlar constitute a geological area known as an ophiolite and are deemed to be of sufficient interest as to merit their own section. Additional sections have been included and the details of these can be found in the list of 'Contents'.

For further information about the individual rocks and minerals mentioned in the different sections of the book, please refer to the index.

The descriptive notes have been kept simple and concentrate on the salient features of the accompanying photograph. For those who wish to study the subject in greater depth, a list of references and further reading is given at the end of the book.

The place where each photograph was taken has been recorded in the respective caption. Maps are included which point out the geographical location of many of the sites and places referred to in this book. At the end of the book, there is a section where the reader can list rocks, minerals and geological features they have identified and where locality and date can be recorded.

Since this book was first published in 2015, more favoured methods of dating rocks have been introduced resulting in changes to the dating of the plutonic intrusions in Shetland including Ronas Hill granite complex.

Introduction to Geology

Our Earth is one of four rocky planets in the solar system, the others being Mercury, Venus and Mars. It consists of four main layers: a solid inner core and a molten outer core, both made of iron and nickel, the semi-molten mantle and the solid crust.

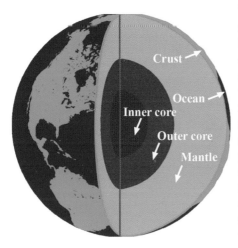

The crust that makes up the Earth's continents is on average 40 km thick, whilst beneath the oceans it is much thinner – only about 8 km thick. The crust is divided into numerous plates, hundreds or even thousands of kilometres across, that move relative to each other on the underlying mantle. These tectonic plates have been, and continue to be, very important in the process of rock formation. As plates move apart, molten rock (magma) from the mantle rises up between them to form new oceanic crust. Where plates move together, oceanic crust plunges back into the mantle where it melts again, feeding volcanoes on the surface above. Continental crust is too thick and buoyant to be dragged down and when continents collide they crumple to produce mountain ranges such as the Himalayas.

All rocks are made up of minerals – crystalline substances, each type with its own characteristic chemical composition and crystal structure. Most rocks are an aggregate of several different kinds of minerals and these provide clues as to how the rock formed. Rocks are classified into three major groups according to how they originated: igneous, sedimentary and metamorphic.

Igneous Rocks. These rocks are formed when magma cools and solidifies. Magma is molten rock that originates from deep inside the Earth. Magma may cool and solidify below the Earth's surface to form intrusive igneous rocks, such as *granite*. Alternatively it may erupt from volcanoes at the Earth's surface as lava and volcanic ash. Igneous rocks formed in this way are called extrusive. A common extrusive igneous rock is *basalt*.

Sedimentary Rocks. These rocks are laid down in layers on the Earth's surface. How they are formed is described below in 'The Rock Cycle'. Sedimentary rocks often contain fossils. Examples of sedimentary rocks are *sandstone* and *limestone*.

Metamorphic Rocks. These are rocks that have been subjected to intense heat and/or pressure which has altered their structure and mineral composition. This can happen to both igneous rocks and sedimentary rocks and also to existing metamorphic rocks. Examples of metamorphic rocks include *slate*, *marble*, *schist* and *gneiss*.

The Rock Cycle. Mountains, and the rocks that form them, seem to breathe an air of permanency, but nothing could be further from the truth! Geology is a dynamic process. Rocks are added to the Earth's surface by crustal movement and molten magma being released by volcanic activity. The exposed rocks are broken down and ground into small particles by the power of wind, waves and ice.

Shetland is subject to repeated battering by wind and waves, which in addition to sea level rise, are slowly reshaping the coastline. © *Dave Donaldson*

These particles are carried by glaciers, rivers and wind and deposited as layers of sediment in lakes, deltas, deserts, and in the sea itself. Buried and compressed, the loose sediments harden in time to form sedimentary rocks such as **clay** or **shale**.

These in turn may be brought back to the Earth's surface or forced deeper down where heat and pressure alter them into metamorphic rocks or melt them to create magma again, bringing us back to where we started!

Right: Burn of Dale, between Scalloway and Lerwick, in spate after heavy rainfall. Such flood events accelerate the transportation and deposition of sediments.

Shetland's Geological Journey

A geological jigsaw

Shetland is a giant geological jigsaw, assembled over hundreds of millions of years from four huge blocks of the Earth's surface as continents collided and then pulled apart again. Each block had a different geological history before they were all brought together by movement along faults, the most important of which is the Great Glen/Walls Boundary Fault system that slices through Scotland and Shetland. In Shetland there are two major offshoots or splays of this fault – the Melby Fault and the Nesting Fault. Periodic movement along the faults, as strain was built up and released, triggered earthquakes and crushed or deformed and altered rocks along the fault zones.

Three billion years in the making

Shetland's oldest rocks formed between 2900 and 2500 million years ago – these 'Archaean gneisses' are over half the age of the Earth! They probably began as igneous rocks, and have been metamorphosed to their present condition by heat and pressure generated in a number of continental collisions which created an early continent known as Laurentia. They spent much of their history buried deep within the Earth's crust but they can be seen exposed in northern parts of Shetland today. They are known as Lewisian gneisses, after the Isle of Lewis in the Western Isles, which is largely made up of rocks from this period. Similar rocks are also found in Northern Canada and Greenland, which tell us that when the rocks formed, Shetland was connected to these land masses.

Our dynamic Earth

Over time, Laurentia eroded and thick layers of sand and mud built up on the seabed around its coast. Nearly 1000 million years ago it collided with several other continents to form a huge supercontinent called Rodinia. During the collision, high temperatures and pressures altered the sand and mud into a range of metamorphic rocks. We call these the rocks of the Moine Supergroup. They can be seen in parts of the Shetland mainland and throughout the island of Yell. Moine rocks include gneisses and schists, sometimes containing minerals such as garnets which form when clay is metamorphosed at high temperatures.

Rodinia began to split apart about 800 million years ago leaving a smaller continent called Vendia, which, in its turn, began to stretch and thin. Layers of sand, silt and iron and aluminium-rich mud were deposited in new marine basins within the continent. Eventually the continent split completely and Laurentia drifted south as a new ocean called Iapetus was born. Magma welled up from the Earth's mantle and solidified to form the floor of the Iapetus Ocean. Evidence of the birth of this new ocean has been identified at Catpund in the south Mainland.

About 490 million years ago another mass collision of continents occurred and by 420 million years ago the Iapetus Ocean finally closed. It was at this time that the rocks of England and Scotland were first united. The sands, silts and muds from the marine basins of Vendia were metamorphosed to form the rocks of the Dalradian Supergroup which make up much of Shetland's central mainland and the western part of Unst. The Dalradian rocks include psammites (metamorphosed impure sandstones), schists, quartzites and limestones. The rocks of the Moine Supergroup were further metamorphosed at this time.

When the Iapetus Ocean closed, the colliding continents were forced upwards to build an enormous mountain chain. The remains of this Caledonian mountain chain can be traced from North America through Greenland, Ireland, Scotland and Scandinavia and form the spine of Shetland today. Rocks of the Moine Supergroup were thrust up over Lewisian basement rocks as the mountains formed. The line of this thrust can be seen in the north Mainland. With the closure of the Iapetus Ocean, some of the Earth's crust and mantle from beneath the ocean was forced up over the top of the Laurentian continent to become part of the newly formed mountains. These oceanic rocks are very different from those that make up the continents and are not usually visible at the Earth's surface, but a section of ocean floor can be seen in the eastern parts of Unst and Fetlar where it was driven up along two major thrusts. An exposed ocean crust such as this is called an ophiolite and Shetland is one of the best places in the world to see one.

Between 465 and 370 million years ago, rocks melting in the roots of the Caledonian mountain chain generated magma that forced its way up into the colder crust to solidify below the surface into granitic bodies called plutons. Tectonic uplift and the erosion of overlying rocks has exposed several of these plutons in various parts of Shetland. Much of Northmavine was formed in this way, including Shetland's highest point, Ronas Hill. Rifting within the mountain chain created sedimentary basins where the Earth's crust was thin enough for magma to force its way to the surface and erupt as volcanoes like the one at Eshaness.

Shetland lay in the eroding foothills of the Caledonian mountains. Boulders, pebbles, sand and mud were washed down from the mountains by fast flowing torrents. At the base of the mountains the gradient eased so the water no longer had the energy to move larger stones and these were dumped. The finer material was carried out into a desert plain by braided rivers and eventually deposited on flood plains and in temporary lakes. Buried and lithified (hardened into rock), these sediments now make up the conglomerates, sandstones and mudstones, formed between 394 and 384 million years ago, that can be seen in the south and west of the islands today. Along with other Scottish rocks of this period they are collectively known as Old Red Sandstone.

Past Environments

Shetland has been on an incredible geological journey, from close to the South Pole, across the Equator, to its current position at the crossroads of the North Atlantic. Through this time the climate and landscape have changed dramatically many times, varying from arid desert to frozen wasteland.

Several times between 1000 and 543 million years ago, global scale glaciations turned our planet into 'Snowball Earth'. The end of each glaciation was marked by a short but extreme period of 'ultra-greenhouse' global warming where the average global surface temperature may have been as high as 50°C. Shetland's metamorphosed limestones contain evidence for this extreme climate change within their chemical make-up.

During the Devonian Period, following the closure of the Iapetus Ocean 420 million years ago, the rocks that are now northern Britain lay just south of the Equator and far inland within a vast desert continent where the climate varied from warm and humid to dry and arid.

Shaping the landscape

The varied landscape that you can see today has developed through the action of wind, ice and water. By around 5 million years ago Shetland lay more or less where we find it today, but global temperatures were higher than at present. In a warm, wet climate, the limestone bands that run through the central mainland were dissolved by rainwater to create the fertile Tingwall valley and the unusual parallel valleys of Pettadale and Weisdale. The 'rotten stone' produced by deep weathering of the valley sides under sub-tropical conditions shows that these valleys were not carved by glaciers but are much older.

During the past 2.5 million years the world has experienced a series of ice ages interspersed with warmer interglacial periods. We are currently enjoying an interglacial, but 100,000 years ago ice from Scandinavia covered Shetland, and 25,000 years ago a more localized icecap covered the central ridge of the islands.

Ice sheets scoured the surface of the land, deepening existing channels between the islands and smoothing the harder uplands of granite. In some cases valleys were carved out by meltwater flowing beneath the ice sheets and glacial till was deposited on the valley floors.

Since the melting of the last ice-cap over Shetland approximately 12,000 years ago, water has filled the valleys and depressions to leave a flooded landscape of islands and inlets (voes). New landforms such as coastal bars and tombolos have built up as the sea has reworked sediments of sand, gravel, pebbles and shingle.

Geological Map of Shetland

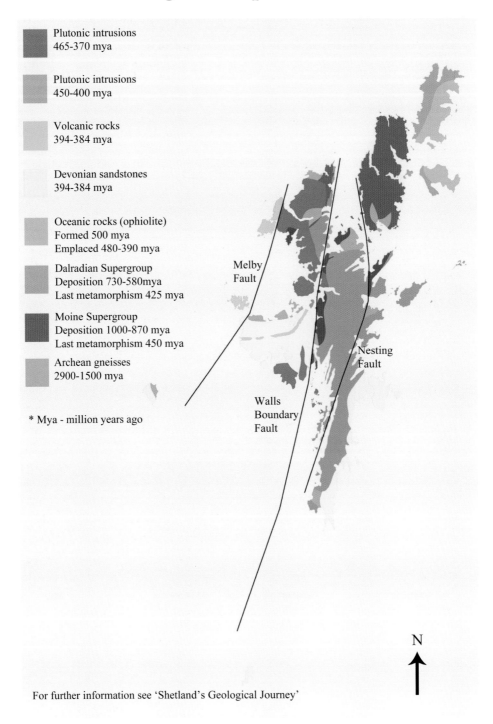

Plutonic intrusions
465-370 mya

Plutonic intrusions
450-400 mya

Volcanic rocks
394-384 mya

Devonian sandstones
394-384 mya

Oceanic rocks (ophiolite)
Formed 500 mya
Emplaced 480-390 mya

Dalradian Supergroup
Deposition 730-580mya
Last metamorphism 425 mya

Moine Supergroup
Deposition 1000-870 mya
Last metamorphism 450 mya

Archean gneisses
2900-1500 mya

* Mya - million years ago

Melby
Fault

Nesting
Fault

Walls
Boundary
Fault

N

For further information see 'Shetland's Geological Journey'

Timeline of Shetland's Geology

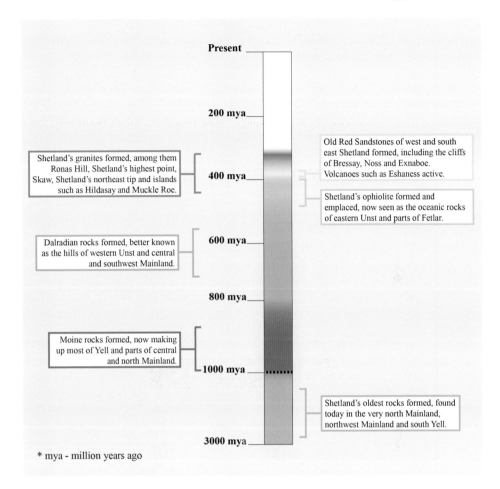

Present

200 mya

Shetland's granites formed, among them Ronas Hill, Shetland's highest point, Skaw, Shetland's northeast tip and islands such as Hildasay and Muckle Roe.

400 mya

Old Red Sandstones of west and south east Shetland formed, including the cliffs of Bressay, Noss and Exnaboe. Volcanoes such as Eshaness active.

Shetland's ophiolite formed and emplaced, now seen as the oceanic rocks of eastern Unst and parts of Fetlar.

Dalradian rocks formed, better known as the hills of western Unst and central and southwest Mainland.

600 mya

800 mya

Moine rocks formed, now making up most of Yell and parts of central and north Mainland.

1000 mya

Shetland's oldest rocks formed, found today in the very north Mainland, northwest Mainland and south Yell.

3000 mya

* mya - million years ago

Geopark Shetland

Shetland is a UNESCO Global Geopark because of its extraordinarily diverse and internationally important geological heritage.

The Geopark concept grew from an idea at the turn of the millennium; a vision of four European territories working in partnership, that geological heritage should be valued, protected and, above all, used sustainably to benefit local communities. In a world where the climate is changing, resources are dwindling and community identity is often lacking, the time was ripe for such an idea. Four Geoparks signed a convention on Lesvos, in Greece, in June 2000 declaring the creation of the European Geoparks Network. Four years later in 2004 a Global Geoparks Network, supported by UNESCO, was born. In 2013 the Global Geoparks welcomed their 100th member, and in 2015 the 195 Member States of UNESCO ratified the creation of a new label, the UNESCO Global Geoparks.

At the time of writing, more than 125 territories around the world are using their outstanding geological heritage to underpin the sustainable development of their regions, largely through education and tourism. Geoparks highlight the close links between geodiversity and cultural and natural heritage, raise awareness of key issues facing society in the context of the dynamic planet we live on and seek to conserve the natural environment.

Geopark Shetland is managed by Shetland Amenity Trust, and brings Shetland's geological story to the widest possible audience, with displays at Shetland Museum and Archives and local Heritage Centres; 'geowalls' at Mavis Grind, Haroldswick and Funzie; exhibits and panels at Braewick and Stennes; self-guided trail packs exploring 'The Shetland ophiolite' and 'Shetland's volcano', as well as geological interpretation other sites of geological importance around the islands.

The 'geowall' at Mavis Grind. © *Billy Fox*

The Geopark Shetland app, for Android and iPhone, introduces users to Geopark Shetland through Google maps populated with information about geological sites of interest. The app is linked to GPS and will alert the user when a site is reached – a useful aid for people who want to explore Shetland's fascinating geology for themselves. Sites can be searched by geological theme, and the app also includes walking trails.

The Geopark supports lifelong learning through school workshops, fieldtrips and night classes. It has helped a number of pupils throughout the isles to gain John Muir Discovery awards. Geopark Shetland is the lead partner in the Shetland Nature Festival that runs annually in collaboration with European Geoparks Week.

Extrusive Igneous Rocks

Shetland's extrusive igneous (volcanic) rocks were erupted during the Devonian Period, between 394 and 384 million years ago. At this time, Shetland was landlocked within a large desert continent close to the Equator. The Eshaness peninsula is the remains of an ancient volcano, and has been described as the best section through the flank of an extinct volcano in the UK.

Basalt, Braewick Beach (west), Eshaness. This rock formed from lava erupted from a large volcano onto a desert plain. Gas bubbles within the lava have been preserved as tiny holes called vesicles within the solid rock (see inset).

Rhyolite and **basalt**, Papa Stour. The pink rock that forms most of the cliff is a single, thick rhyolite lava flow. The grey rocks to the bottom left are a series of basalt lava flows. Basalt lava is thin and runny and thus forms thin beds of lava, whilst the rhyolite is thick and sticky and forms thick layers. © Jonathan Swale

Lava layers, Brei Geo, Eshaness. The cliff face displays alternating black and red layers which represent layer upon layer of lava flows. The different colours are caused by weathering of the surface of each lava layer before deposition of the next one.

Agglomerate, Kirn o Slettans, Eshaness. This formed from lumps of solid rock that were ripped from the walls of a volcanic vent and thrown up into the air during large explosive eruptions. The lumps of rock are known as volcanic blocks if over 64 mm in diameter and volcanic bombs if under 64 mm diameter.

Ignimbrite, Grind o da Navir, Eshaness.   This rock was formed from pyroclastic flows – searingly hot clouds of gas, droplets of molten lava and pumice fragments that raced down the side of the volcano. When the cloud settled the lava drops were squashed into candle flame shapes called fiammé which can be seen as small orange streaks within the rock.

Lahar, Braewick Beach (west), Eshaness.   This is a volcanic mudflow – a mixture of volcanic rock fragments, ash and water with the consistency of cement that flowed down the volcano at high speed. Lahars can flow tens of metres per second, destroying everything in their path.

Stennes. The area surrounding the beach and the beach itself is composed of andesitic rock and andesitic tuff. The following four photographs are examples of rocks found on the beach.

Porphyritic andesite, Beach of Stennes, Eshaness.

Rhyolite with **amygdales** (filled vesicles), Beach of Stennes, Eshaness.   The gas bubbles within this rock have been filled with fine grained silica (chalcedony). In cases where banding of different minerals occurs within the vesicles, agates can be found.

Agate in **andesite**, Beach of Stennes, Eshaness.   When lava erupts from a volcanic vent it contains bubbles of gas or steam which solidify into small cavities called vesicles. Water percolating through the cooled rock deposits minerals in the vesicles, filling them with milky white crystals or sometimes banded agates. © *Billy Fox*

Volcanic blocks in **lava**, Beach of Stennes, Eshaness.   The blocks are fragments of rock that have been blasted from the volcano in a solid state.

Intrusive Igneous Rocks

Most of Shetland's plutonic rocks were intruded into the base of the Caledonian mountains between 465 and 370 million years ago. Our youngest intrusive rocks are the dykes that can be seen cutting across the Ronas Hill granite.

Granite, Braewick Beach (east), Eshaness.   Granite is made of feldspar, quartz and mica. In this case the colour of the rock is due to a large proportion of pink feldspar.

Granite, Braewick Beach (east), Eshaness.   Because granite crystallizes slowly beneath the Earth's surface, the crystals have grown large enough to be seen with the naked eye. Here we can see individual crystals of pink and white feldspar, grey mica and glassy quartz.

Granite. Skaw Beach, Unst.   Skaw granite is notable for its spectacular large pink feldspar crystals (see inset). The groundmass is finer grained quartz, mica and creamy feldspar.

Granite. Fuglaness, West Burra. Similar to the Skaw granite but the feldspar crystals are not so large and widely spaced (see inset). This is probably due to its having cooled and crystalised under different conditions.

Monzonite, Fuglaness, West Burra.   This rock is made up mostly of pink and cream feldspar and dark pyroxene (see inset). This occurs next to the Fuglaness granite and has similar mineral composition but much smaller crystals, probably indicating that it formed at the edge of the melt and cooled more quickly.

Gabbro boulder sitting on **granite**, Böd Ayre, Busta. Gabbro is made of white feldspar and dark pyroxene, but no quartz, giving it a grey speckled appearance. Here it is seen contrasted with pink granite (see inset).

Boulder, beach at Easter Quarff.　This shows the junction between a granite intrusion and the grey metamorphic rock into which it was injected.

1 cm

Net veining of **granite** and **gabbro**, beach at Nibon.　The grey gabbro cooled and solidified before molten pink granite was injected into fractures in the rock.

Diorite, Nibon. This intrusive igneous rock usually forms plutons deep in the Earth's crust. It is composed principally of plagioclase feldspar with lesser amounts of hornblende and biotite. If a magma with the same chemical composition as diorite makes it all the way up to erupt at the surface, the resulting rock is andesite. This image shows a granite vein (inset), which is a common feature of this area.

Granite and **gabbro** mixing, Virdins Quarry, Mavis Grind. Here the pink granite magma was injected whilst the grey gabbro magma was still fluid, resulting in partial mixing of the two. The process is complex and not well understood (see inset). On the left of the inset photo there are distinct veins of granite that must have been injected into solid gabbro whilst in the foreground of the picture the gabbro was still fluid, resul-ing in mixing.

Xenolith in Skaw **granite**, Skaw Beach, Unst. A xenolith is a lump of solid rock that has been completely surrounded by molten magma, in this case Skaw granite.

Pink rhyolite dykes cutting through **gneiss**, Wilgi Geos, east of Uyea, Northmavine.   Granite and gabbro are coarse-grained rocks where the magma cools slowly. However, magma can be injected into fissures in cold rock, in which case it cools and crystallises quickly, resulting in fine grained rock, in this case rhyolite. © *Billy Fox*

Basalt dyke in granite. Heoganeap, east of Uyea, Northmavine. These dykes and the rhyolite dykes on the previous page are part of the dyke swarm that cuts across the Ronas Hill granite. © *Jonathan Swale*

Pegmatites

A pegmatite is often formed from the last of the magma to solidify. This contains a lot of volatiles and is very fluid. As a result, it is easily injected into other rocks to form veins, but unlike the rhyolite in dykes, the crystals grow extremely large. Pegmatites tend to have a granite composition of glassy quartz, pink or white feldspar and dark mica, and sometimes contain unusual minerals as the rarer elements in the magma are concentrated in them. The following photographs are examples of pegmatites.

Pegmatite, Muckle Roe.

Pegmatite, Easter Quarff.

Pegmatite, Port Arthur, Scalloway.

Pink **pegmatite** veins, Easter Quarff. Vein surface exposed on the shore (see inset).

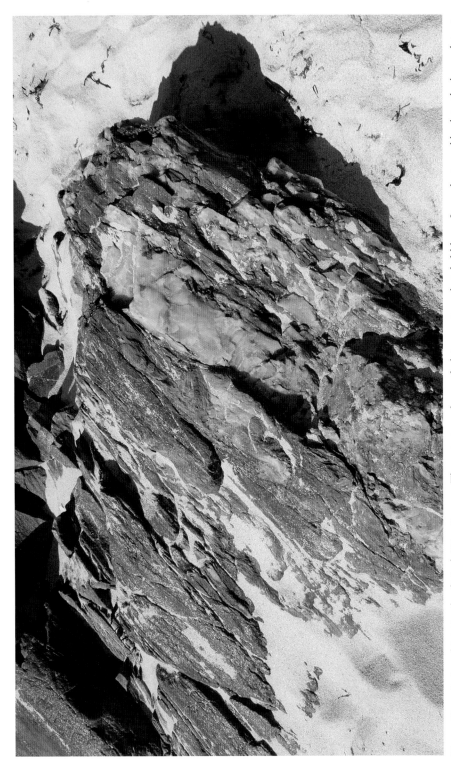

Pegmatite vein in **schist**, Sands of Meal, West Burra. The vein is made up of white quartz and pink feldspar. It can be traced back to the large plutonic body that represents the source magma.

Sedimentary Rocks

Shetland's sedimentary rocks formed during the Devonian Period. This lasted from 416 million years ago to 359 million years ago, although Shetland's Devonian rocks were actually formed between 394 and 384 million years ago. Sedimentary rocks in Scotland that formed during the Devonian are collectively known as Old Red Sandstone, to distinguish them from a younger group of sedimentary rocks known as New Red Sandstone (which does not occur in Shetland). It should be noted that most of Shetland's Old Red Sandstone, as seen in the photographs that follow, is not actually red!

Sandstone, Braewick Beach (west), Eshaness.   The sandy layers that built up nearly 400 million years ago to form this rock can clearly be seen. The red colour is caused by iron oxide coating the sand grains.

Banded sandstone. Braewick Beach (west), Eshaness. This rock was formed from sandy sediments laid down in an ancient lake. The pattern of different colours represent different mineral compositions. The grey layers react with hydrochloric acid, indicating carbonate content. This rock occurs nowhere else in Shetland and its method of formation remains a bit of a mystery.

Coarse-grained Sandstone, Sands of Sound, Lerwick.   These rocks formed when Shetland lay just south of the Equator and far inland, in the foothills of the Caledonian Mountains. The mountains were fast eroding and their sandy sediments were transported by braided rivers and deposited onto a vast desert plain (see inset for detail of sandy layers).

Sandstone, Sands of Sound, Lerwick.   The pebbles within the sandstone, which follow a gentle curve in the central part of the photograph, were transported and deposited as a result of fast flowing water, either in the bed of a stream, or in a flood event.

Conglomerate, Ness of Burgi, Scatness. Boulders, pebbles, and finer sediments were washed down the Caledonian Mountains by fast-flowing rivers. When they reached the plain, the larger stones were dumped at the foot of the mountains in fan-shaped deposits of conglomerate called alluvial fans. The alluvial fans were reworked as rivers flowed across them, transporting and re-depositing the sediments. We see the result at the Ness of Burgi where layers of conglomerate alternate with layers of finer sediment (see inset for detail).

Lake sediments, Shingly Geo, Exnaboe.   Beds made up of thin layers of fine sediment and impure limestone seen in the lower part of this photograph represent a lake. The blocky upper layers represent sandstones deposited by rivers.

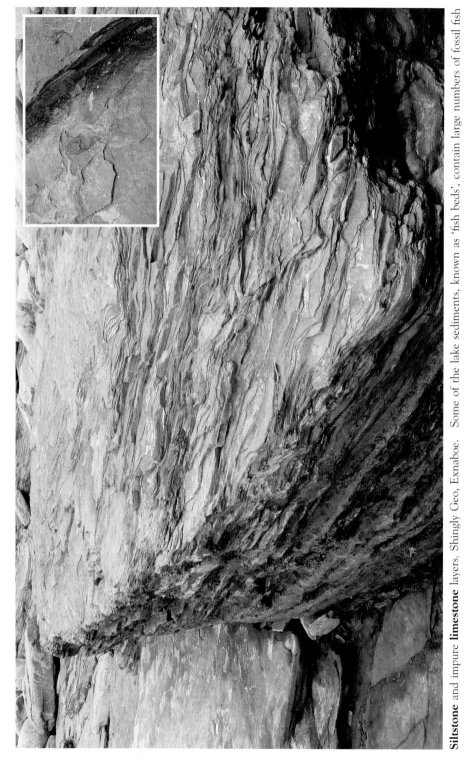

Siltstone and impure **limestone** layers, Shingly Geo, Exnaboe. Some of the lake sediments, known as 'fish beds', contain large numbers of fossil fish (see inset).

Breccia, Fladdabister.   This rock is made up of broken rock fragments that formed scree on the slopes of the Caledonian Mountains. It has now solidified (lithified) into solid rock and is no longer active, so can be referred to as 'fossil' scree.

Breccia boulder, beach at Easter Quarff. Jagged fragments of different rocks can be seen within this boulder which formed from fossilised scree. Breccia is made up of angular fragments of other rock – such as this piece of granite – an igneous rock (see inset).

Granite pebble in **coarse-grained sandstone**, Sands of Sound, Lerwick. Occasionally, isolated pebbles or layers of pebbles have been carried out into the desert and incorporated into sandstone.

Breccia and **sandstone** layers, Maywick Beach.   One of the rocks in the coastal defences is probably from the Brindister Quarry. The lower part is thinly bedded red sandstone, on top of which is a breccia made up of small rock fragments in a sandstone matrix.

Metamorphic Rocks

Most of Shetland is made of metamorphic rocks and they are more varied in age and variety than the other rocks of Shetland. The rock that results from metamorphism depends on the nature of the original rock, and the level of heat and pressure to which it has been subjected (this is known as the metamorphic grade). Metamorphism introduces a texture into rocks as the mineral crystals align themselves perpendicularly to the main stress.

Metamorphic Grade

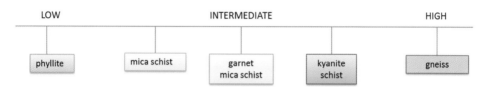

This shows the relative position of the rocks, and not their absolute position, on the metamorphic grade scale

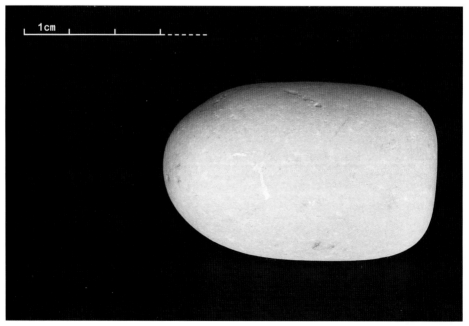

Quartzite, Beach of Newgarth, Westing, Unst.   This rock began life as sandstone – a sedimentary rock made mainly of quartz grains. Quartz is chemically unaffected by heat and pressure but the grains have intergrown, making the metamorphic rock much tougher than the original.

Semi-pelite, Beach of Newgarth, Westing, Unst.   This is a form of schist that was originally an impure sandstone. The original sedimentary layering on the flat surface – light sandy layers and darker muddy layers – can still be seen. Metamorphism has produced alternating bands of white quartz and dark mica that cut across the original layers (see inset).

Phyllite, Scord of Scalloway. Metamorphism of rocks made of clay minerals produces a variety of different rocks depending on the degree of heat and pressure to which they have been subjected. Phyllite is a low grade metamorphic rock. Typically it has well-developed foliation and fractures into leaf-like pieces, from which the name 'phyllite' is derived. Mica and chlorite are essential constituents and their presence gives the rock a characteristic greenish-grey sheen, the chlorite imparting the greeny tinge and mica the darker.

Phyllite, Maywick Beach (east). The bluish colour of the phyllite in this photograph is due to the way light is reflected from the plates of mica, which in turn depends on their angulation. The inset shows 'strain bands', where the angulation of the mica plates is different from the remainder of the rock.

Mica schist, beach at Easter Quarff. At the metamorphic grade above phyllite, clay minerals are altered to mica. The plate-like crystals of mica align perpendicularly to the stress to which the rock has been subjected. As a result, the rock splits easily in one direction. The name schist is from the Greek 'to split'.

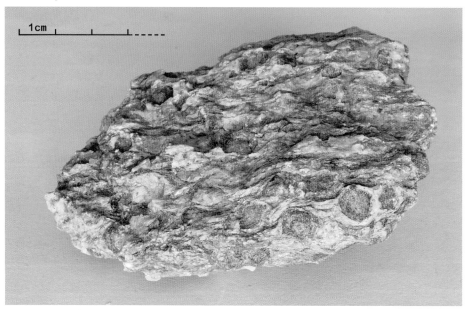

Garnet mica schist, Ness of Hillswick. At the next stage of metamorphism of clay minerals, beautiful garnets are formed amongst the mica crystals. Usually these occur as clusters of small crystals. Occasionally large single crystals can be found, which can be polished into gemstones, but these are very rare in Shetland.

Kyanite schist, Stromness, Muckle Roe.   At still higher grades, minerals such as pale blue blades of kyanite, staurolite and sillimanite form. © *Allen Fraser*

Gneiss, beach at Easter Quarff.   At the highest grade of metamorphism the rock separates out into pale bands of silica-rich minerals and darker bands of iron-rich minerals. This is a gneiss. Some sources say the word originates from the Middle High German gneist meaning 'to spark' because the rock glitters. Within this rock you can see examples of 'boudinage' which is the result of stretching of the layers within the rock. The silica-rich bands are strong and have broken into discrete pods known as boudins whilst the weaker dark bands have stretched and bent around them.

Granite gneiss, beach at Easter Quarff.　This is an orthogneiss, i.e. the original rock was igneous – in this case granite. The mineral composition has remained much the same, but the mineral crystals have aligned perpendicularly to the stress to give it a banded appearance.

Lewisian gneiss, Uyea, Northmavine.　This comes from the oldest rock formation in Shetland. Originally a granite, it has been subjected to many periods of metamorphism and developed very strong banding. © *Billy Fox*

Augen gneiss, disused quarry near Hill of Lee, Gonfirth.   This rock originated in a major shear zone between Shetland's Moine and Dalradian rocks. The original crystal structure of the rock was destroyed by shearing movement and new minerals have formed, including large feldspar crystals, known as 'augen', from the German for eyes (see inset).

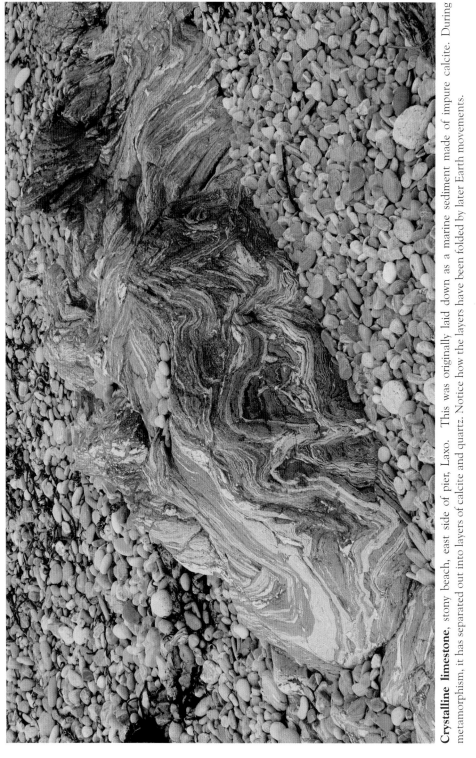

Crystalline limestone, stony beach, east side of pier, Laxo. This was originally laid down as a marine sediment made of impure calcite. During metamorphism, it has separated out into layers of calcite and quartz. Notice how the layers have been folded by later Earth movements.

The Shetland Ophiolite

The rocks of eastern Unst and Fetlar require some special explanation.

Between 490 and 420 million years ago, two continents collided and the ocean between them vanished. Part of the floor of the ocean was caught up in the collision and thrust on top of one of the continents. This ocean floor forms the eastern part of Unst and much of Fetlar today. An exposed section of ocean floor is known as an ophiolite. The rocks were originally igneous – formed from molten rock beneath the ancient Iapetus Ocean.

The ophiolite consists of a sequence of rocks of varying mineral composition, including harzburgite, dunite, wehrlite and pyroxenite. All of these rocks contain the minerals olivine and pyroxene in varying proportions. These rocks have been metamorphosed by hot fluids circulating through them and altering much of the olivine to the mineral serpentine, so for simplicity we often refer to these as serpentine rocks. Above these in the sequence are gabbro and basalt – rocks made mainly of pyroxene and feldspar.

The dunite, harzburgite and gabbro in Unst and Fetlar has been partially metamorphosed and strictly speaking should be referred to as meta-dunite, meta-harzburgite and meta-gabbro but the term 'meta' is often omitted in practice and will be omitted throughout this book. It is very difficult for the non-geologist to distinguish between harzburgite, dunite and wehrlite in the field – another reason why the term serpentine is so useful.

In some places the olivine has been so altered that it has gone beyond serpentine to become the mineral talc (see Rocks, Minerals and Man section).

The Taing, Norwick, Unst. The small headland marks the boundary between oceanic and continental crust. The Hill of Clibberswick in the distance is part of the ophiolite.

Harzburgite, Muckle Heog, Unst.   Harzburgite originated in the Earth's mantle deep beneath the Iapetus Ocean. It is made up of soft olivine and the much harder mineral orthopyroxene and differential weathering of the two minerals gives it a slightly nobbly texture. The ochre colour is due to weathering – a fresh surface would be dark greyish-green.

Dunite, Keen of Hamar, Unst.   Dunite formed above the harzburgite in the Iapetus Ocean crust and is made up mainly of soft olivine. It is difficult to distinguish from harzburgite in the field but dunite tends to have a smoother surface due to the lack of orthopyroxene. Because olivine is much softer than orthopyroxene, the dunite weathers more quickly than the harzburgite, which is why harzburgite forms the hills and dunite the lower ground.

Antigorite (serpentine mineral), Keen of Hamar, Unst.   There are a number of different serpentine minerals including antigorite, lizardite, and chrysotile (asbestos). Sometimes microscopic analysis is required to be certain of identification. The surrounding rock contains pyroxene, indicating that it is harzburgite.

Dunite, Keen of Hamar, Unst.   It is likely that this is a fractured surface that cracked along a small vein of serpentinite. Fresh rock surfaces are greyish-green in colour and weather to a rusty brown.

Dark green **serpentinite** with bands of paler **talc**, Norwick Beach, Unst.

Gabbro, Uyeasound, Unst.   This rock is a mixture of dark pyroxene crystals and white feldspar crystals. © *Jonathan Swale*

Funzie Conglomerate, beach of Funzie, Fetlar.   Conglomerate is a rock made up of water-worn boulders and pebbles, with finer sediments filling the spaces between them. The Funzie conglomerate is unusual because after deposition it was caught up between two sections of the Shetland ophiolite as it was thrust over the continent. The stress distorted the originally round cobbles of quartz, granite and greenschist into rods, like cigars, sometimes twenty times their original length. The mud and sand between them was metamorphosed by heat and pressure to become phyllite.

Conglomerate cliffs, Ness of Funzie, Fetlar.   Following the coast from beach of Funzie to Staves Geo, the conglomerate cobbles become more and more deformed as one approaches the boundary with the upper block of ophiolite. This gives the rock a layered appearance that is visible in cliff faces along the way. The layering is parallel to the direction of thrusting.

Landscape

Keen of Hamar, Unst.   This is an extensive area of gravelly soil made up of weathered fragments of partially serpentinised durite (known as serpentine debris). It is little altered since the end of the last glaciation 12,000 years ago. Water drains quickly through the soil and shattered bedrock beneath, so that drought-like conditions are common. The debris is home to several arctic-alpine plants adapted to these unusual conditions. They include Shetland Mouse-ear (often called Edmondston's Chickweed), a variety of Arctic Mouse-ear endemic to Unst (see inset).

Calder's Geo, Eshaness.   This coastline cuts through the remains of an extinct volcano, active some 395 million years ago. The cliffs are formed from layers of ash, lava and agglomerate. The island visible in the distance is believed to be the remains of the main volcanic vent.

Brei Geo, Eshaness.   The upper part of the cliffs here are eroding back due to a weak layer in the rock and as a consequence exposing a dramatically domed lava flow.

Grind o da Navir, Eshaness.   Ignimbrite reflected in a pool of water. In stormy weather, this location is exposed to the full force of the North Atlantic which washes up a natural ramp from sea level 20 m below and rears huge blocks from the bedrock. The pale surfaces of the blocks in the top left of the photograph are fresh and show the most recent damage.

Dore Holm, Eshaness. One of the most striking of Shetland's natural arches. Formed from the volcanic rock andesite, this coastal feature is often likened to a drinking horse or an elephant – all in the eye of the beholder!

Braewick, Eshaness.　Note granite cliffs on the left. In the distance, on the right, are granite stacks known as Da Drongs.

Braewick Beach, Eshaness.   The east end of the beach is notable for the large expanse of glacial till sitting above the granite bedrock (see inset).

Ronas Hill. At 450 m, Shetland's highest point is formed from distinctive red granite that was intruded into the Earth's crust about 427 million years ago and has been exposed due to erosion of overlying rocks.

Nibon. An extensive area of land between Mangaster Voe and Gunnister Voe is composed of diorite. For more details, see section on Igneous Intrusive Rocks, and under 'Diorite'.

Tingwall Valley. Broad parallel bands of limestone run north-south down the central mainland giving rise to some of Shetland's most fertile districts: Weisdale, Whiteness and Tingwall. The limestone formed from sediments deposited in an ancient ocean called Iapetus about 500 million years ago. All the limestone in Shetland has been partially metamorphosed and strictly speaking should be referred to as crystalline limestone. However, since the expression limestone is widely used and referred to, the authors have opted to use it in preference to the less commonly used, albeit more accurate term, crystalline limestone.

Sandstone cliffs of Noss. The sandstone of Bressay and Noss formed nearly 400 million years ago as the Caledonian Mountains eroded and deposited their sediments into rivers and lakes on a large desert plain. The sandstone has eroded to form ledges that are ideal nesting sites for seabird colonies.

Gannets nesting on honeycomb-weathered sandstone, Noss.

Giant's Leg, Bressay.   This impressive natural arch has been eroded from sandstone. The different coloured layers are due to the varied mineral composition of the sediments.

Gaada Stack, Foula. The sandstone layers show that these rocks have been tilted by earth movements since the layers of sediment would originally have been deposited horizontally.

Broken Brough, Exnaboe. The cliffs here are ancient sand-dune fields that compacted to form sandstone nearly 400 million years ago. The pattern in the cliff face is known as 'cross-bedding' and helps to identify the direction in which the dunes formed and therefore the direction of the prevailing winds.

Ness of Burgi, Scatness.   The sequence of sand, pebbles and cobbles that are exposed in the cliffs, eroded from the Caledonian mountains nearly 395 million years ago, and were laid down by braided rivers.

Non-conformity, north end of the Bay of Fladdabister.   A junction between two rock types that represents a gap in time is called a non-conformity. At the base of this photograph are tilted psammites (metamorphosed sandstones) that were part of the huge Caledonian mountain chain that formed just over 400 million years ago. The psammites eroded for some time before scree from higher slopes was deposited on top of their eroded s rface to form new sedimentary rock. © *Billy Fox*

Rocks, Minerals and Man

There is evidence that Shetland's inhabitants have made extensive use of the islands' rocks and minerals since human settlement began.

The diversity of rocks and minerals has provided residents with a variety of resources with a wide range of uses. Six thousand years ago, early settlers found quartz to be an invaluable substitute for flint to make arrowheads. Two thousand years later, felsite was being used to make polished weapons for ceremonial purposes. Between 600 BC and 100 AD, Iron Age builders exploited local stone to build over 100 stone towers or brochs. Soapstone was used extensively, particularly during the Norse period, and is described in more detail below (see page 82). In the 19th and 20th centuries, limestone was roasted to create lime for building and agricultural purposes. Today, the process of exploitation continues with numerous quarries producing talc, sandstone and crushed rock for a variety of uses.

Shetland's metal ores have been exploited for the last 2,500 years with archaeological excavations frequently turning up evidence of metal working. Copper and iron mines were worked in southern parts of Shetland between 1790 and 1920, most notable being the Sand Lodge mine in Sandwick. About 10,000 tonnes of magnetite was mined near Sullom Voe between 1954 and 1957 with an estimated 20,000 tons still remaining. Farther north, chromite deposits were extracted from opencast quarries on the island of Unst – some 50,000 tons, between 1820 and 1944. Semi-precious stones such as garnets can be found in Shetland's metamorphic rocks, whilst traces of gold and platinum are known to occur in the North Isles.

Drystane dyke, Haroldswick, Unst.   Harzburgite stone obtained from nearby. Distinctive ochre colour is due to weathering.

Drystane dyke, South Nesting.   The stone used here is schist.

Ruined croft house, Fladdabister.   Sandstone is easily quarried in flat surfaced blocks that make excellent building stone.

Ruined croft house, Lunnaness.　The blocky stones are quartzite and the flatter ones are schist.

Ruined house, Minn, West Burra. 'Beach harl' (concrete made from beach pebbles) was used as building material (for detail, see inset).

Beware! Not everything that looks like a rock is a rock! Concrete block, Skaw Beach, Unst. This block has been mixed using dunite.

A block of cement, Isbister, North Roe. To the uninitiated, appearances can be deceiving! Clues that may help to distinguish such a block of cement from natural rock are as follows: close inspection may show the unbroken edges to be moulded into a rounded shape, there may be remnants of the original outer paper packaging adherent to the surface of the block or lying about nearby, the presence of similar blocks nearby and the proximity to either human habitation or a place of human activity.

Working phyllite quarry, Scalloway. This local rock has many uses including road metal and construction.

Disused soapstone quarry, Catpund, Cunningsburgh.   The Shetland word for soapstone is 'kleber', and it has been described as Shetland's oldest industry dating back to the late fourth millennium BC (Neolithic period). When fresh, soapstone is soft and easily carved. It is also amenable to firing which makes it hard and non-porous. This in turn increases its usefulness. The quarry at Catpund was extensively used by the Norse inhabitants of Shetland to make a range of domestic objects including bakeplates, bowls, fishing sinkers, loomweights and spindle whorls. A piece of soapstone is shown in the inset.

Working talc quarry, Clibberswick, Unst. This talc is relatively low grade and used primarily as a bulking agent.

Lumps of talc (white) and serpentinite (green). The talc is soft and in places has crumbled into a gritty mélange.

Talc awaiting shipment, Baltasound Pier, Unst (October 2013). A piece of talc is shown in the inset.

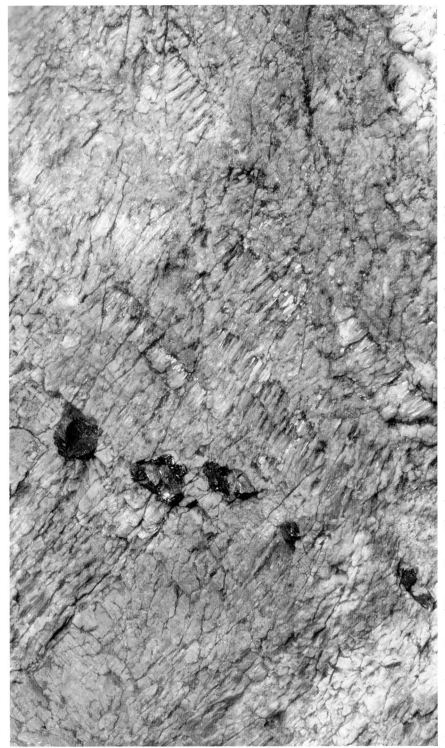

Chromite in dunite, Keen of Hamar, Unst. The chromite appears as black specks within the dunite. In the 19th century, Hagdale in Unst was the largest chromite quarry in the UK. The chromite was used as yellow pigment in paint, and in tanning salts.

A 32-metre long ore deposit, Garths Ness, by Quendale. This deposit, which contains iron sulphide (pyrrhotite) with some copper-iron sulphide (chalcopyrite) was briefly mined in the early 19th century.

Miscellaneous Rocks

Dry/Wet

Fine grained gneiss, Minn Beach, West Burra.   When wet (above), appears as an attractive, deep, ebony black colour, but when dried out (below), is a dull grey.

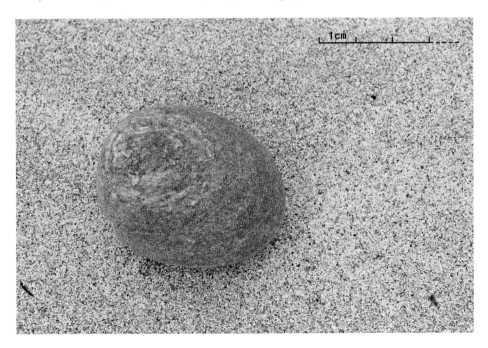

Surface Colouration

The true colour and shade of many rocks is obscured by the presence of externally occurring agents, the most abundant and widespread being numerous species of lichens which may cover rocks partially or completely. Lichens are typically black, grey, white or yellow. Rocks may also be stained or discoloured by algae (which includes seaweeds), which are generally green, brown or red in colour. The following photographs show some examples of these.

Lichens   Skaw Beach.

Lichens   Beach at Grutness.

Lichens   Muckle Roe.

Lichens   Drystane dyke, Easter Quarff.

Algae Low tide, beach at Easter Quarff.

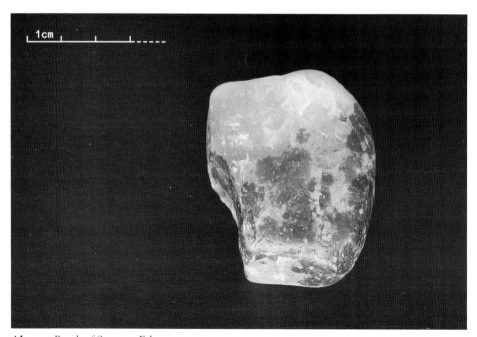

Algae Beach of Stennes, Eshaness.

Algae　Maywick Beach (east).

Iron Staining

Acidic bog water can leach iron out of rocks. When the water comes into contact with air (oxygen), the iron oxidises and precipitates out of the water as brown iron oxide. This can stain the surface of any rocks it flows over.

Iron Staining   Beach at Easter Quarff.

Iron Staining   Beach at Easter Quarff.

Iron Staining   Beach at Easter Quarff.

Iron Staining   Beach at Easter Quarff.

Iron Staining   Muckle Ayre, Muckle Roe.   Below: shows the same rock after the iron oxide has been removed by phosphoric acid. We are grateful to Billy Moore of Scalloway for demonstrating the 'phosphoric acid effect'.

Turbidite

Turbidites are rocks produced as a result of underwater landslides on the continental slope, where the shallow seabed on the edge of the continents slopes down to the deep ocean floor. Loose sediment deposited on the continental shelf by rivers periodically becomes unstable and slides off down the slope. The landslide comes to a stop at the bottom of the slope as a jumbled mass of particles of all sizes. Mud and silt that was suspended in the water by the movement then settles out on top of this, thus each turbidite unit consists of a thick layer of unsorted, coarse sediment overlain by fine sediment.

Turbidite   Beach at St Ninian's Isle (east).

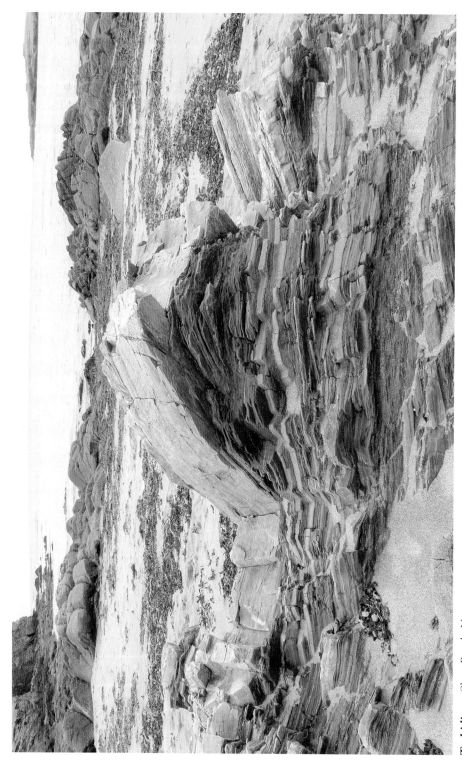

Turbidite Skaw Beach, Unst.

Hydrothermal veins

These are made from minerals deposited from hot water circulating through fractures in the rock. As water cools, minerals crystallise out, the least soluble being deposited first and closest to the source of heat. The commonest veins in Shetland are composed of the mineral quartz. The following photographs are examples of veins.

Hydrothermal Veins   Skaw, Unst.

Hydrothermal Veins   Near Round Loch, Lunnaness.

1 cm

Hydrothermal Veins   Hill of Berry, Scalloway.

Weathering

Many minerals react slowly with air and water so that the exposed surfaces of rocks can be discoloured, making it difficult to tell which minerals the rocks are formed from. These three photographs show granite at various stages of weathering.

Weathering   Granite, Braewick Beach (east), Eshaness.

Weathering   Granite, Muckle Roe, road to Hams.

Weathering Granite, Braewick Beach (west), Eshaness. Unlike the east end of the Braewick Beach, the west end has no igneous intrusive bedrock. What is shown in this photograph is a weathered glacial erratic which has been transported from somewhere else by ice.

Glossary of Geological Terms

Words that appear in italics are explained elsewhere in the glossary. Also, many of the words are further explained throughout the text.

Acid rock	– igneous rock with high silica content, e.g. granite.
Agglomerate	– a *pyroclastic* rock made up of fragments of volcanic rocks which are greater than 64 mm in size and are the result of volcanic explosions. Fragments of *country rocks* may be present.
Ayre	– a long, narrow spit of shingle or sand most often formed across a shallow bay or across a voe, cutting off, either completely or partially, a sheet of water from the sea.
Basement rocks	– the oldest rocks recognised in a given area.
Basic rock	– igneous rock that has low silica content and is quartz free, e.g. basalt.
Braided river	– a river with multiple, small, shallow channels that divide and recombine many times to form a pattern rather like a braid, with islands of sediment between them.
Breccia	– a sedimentary rock containing angular rock fragments which are greater than 2 mm across.
Clast	– mineral particles of sediment ranging from sand grains to boulders.
Conglomerate	– a course-grained sedimentary rock composed of rounded fragments embedded in a matrix of cementing material such as silica.
Country rock	– rock surrounding an igneous *intrusion* or below a lava flow.
Dalradian Supergroup	– a group of metamorphosed sediments laid down in Scotland and Ireland between approximately 800 and 600 million years ago. The term has both geographical and chronological significance.
Dyke	– a sheet-like body of igneous rock which cuts across existing rock structures.
Erratic	– rock transported by a glacier and deposited on the Earth's surface some distance from its origin. Often, the rock type is different from the rock which it overlies.
Fault	– a plane of fracture in a rock along which displacement has occurred.
Intrusion	– a body of igneous rock which has forced itself into pre-existing rock.
Lithosphere	– The upper part of the Earth which includes the crust and the uppermost part of the mantle.
Mineral	– a naturally occurring, inorganic substance that has a crystalline structure. Each mineral has characteristic properties such as hardness, colour, lustre, cleavage and each has a characteristic

chemical composition, e.g. the mineral quartz is silicon dioxide (SiO2). Minerals are the components of rocks.

Moine Supergroup – an association of three meta-sedimentary groups that form a large proportion of the rocks cropping out at the surface of the northern Highlands of Scotland and also parts of Shetland.

Pillow lava – pods of cooled lava that have the rounded appearance of pillows. Formed when liquid lava is poured out into or under the sea and the outer surface cools quickly. This forms a skin and the inner lava remains in a liquid state for longer.

Pluton – mass of igneous rock that has formed beneath the surface of the Earth by the consolidation of magma.

Porphyritic – a textural term describing igneous rocks containing relatively large crystals set in a finer grained groundmass.

Pyroclastic – means 'fire-broken' and is rock formed from the debris of an explosive volcanic eruption. *Agglomerate* and *tuff* are examples of pyroclastic rocks.

Radiocarbon dating – technique for finding the age of organic remains formed in the recent past. Relies on the measurement of the decay of carbon-14 atoms found in all living organisms.

Radioisotope dating – dating of rocks by measuring the different isotopes of elements within the rocks and comparing them to known rates of decay of radioactive isotopes.

Rifting – a process that occurs when the Earth's crust and *lithosphere* are pulled apart by tectonic forces.

Sediments Scale – Boulder (>256 mm)
Cobble (64-256 mm)
Gravel (2-64 mm)
Sand (0.062-2.0 mm)
Silt & clay (mud)

Sill – a sheet-like body of igneous rock intruded along the bedding or structural plane of earlier host rocks.

Till – sediment laid down directly from ice, either underneath or at the margins of ice bodies. Till usually consists of a wide range of sediments from boulders to mud.

Tombolo – an *ayre* which joins an off-shore island to a larger island.

Tuff – a fine-grained, *pyroclastic* rock formed from volcanic ash that has become compacted and lithified. The ash produced by the original explosive volcanic activity may have been borne hundreds of kilometres by winds so that tuff is often formed a long distance from its source.

Ultrabasic rock – igneous rocks with low silica content and consisting almost entirely of ferromagnesian minerals, e.g. peridotite.

Vesicle – gas-bubble cavity in lava, left as a hole after the lava solidifies.

Xenolith – an inclusion of pre-existing rock in an igneous rock.

References

Forster, A. K. & Turner, V.E. (2009). *Kleber: Shetland's Oldest Industry*. Shetland Amenity Trust.

Pellant, C. (1992, 2000). *Rocks and Minerals*. Dorling Kindersley Limited, London.

Roberts, J.L. (2004). *Minerals, Rocks and Fossils*. New Holland Publishers (UK) Ltd.

Park, G. (2010). *Introducing Geology*. Dunedin Academic Press Ltd.

Mykura, W. (1976). *British Regional Geology Orkney and Shetland*. Her Majesty's Stationery Office.

Scottish Geodiversity Forum – http://www.scottishgeology.com/

Geopark Shetland website – www.geoparkshetland.org.uk

Further Reading

Fraser, A., *Precambrian to Present: Shetland's Voyage through Geological Time*. Shetland Amenity Trust (to be published).

McKirdy, A., Gordon., J. & Crofts, R. (2007). *Land of Mountains and Flood*. Birlinn Limited (in association with Scottish Natural Heritage).

British Geological Survey – www.bgs.ac.uk
Supplier of the 1:50000 **solid** geology maps of Shetland; for the serious student of Shetland's bedrock geology, these maps are an indispensable tool.

Scottish Natural Heritage (2010) *Landscape fashioned by geology – Orkney and Shetland.*

Geological Sites and Places of Interest – Northern Isles

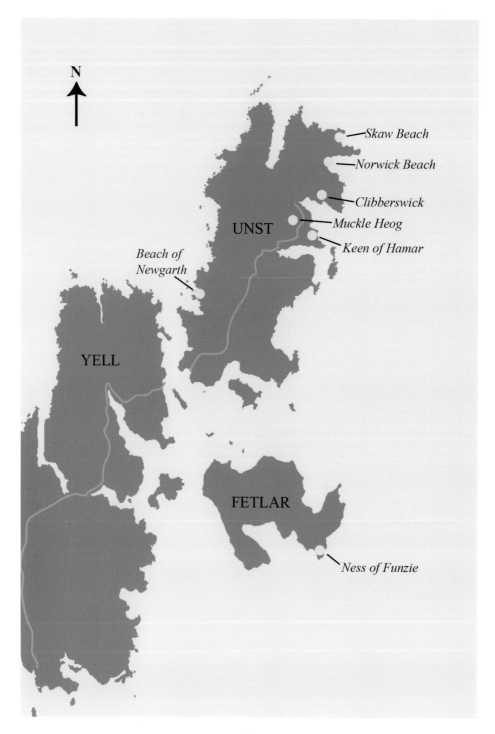

Geological Sites and Places of Interest – North Mainland

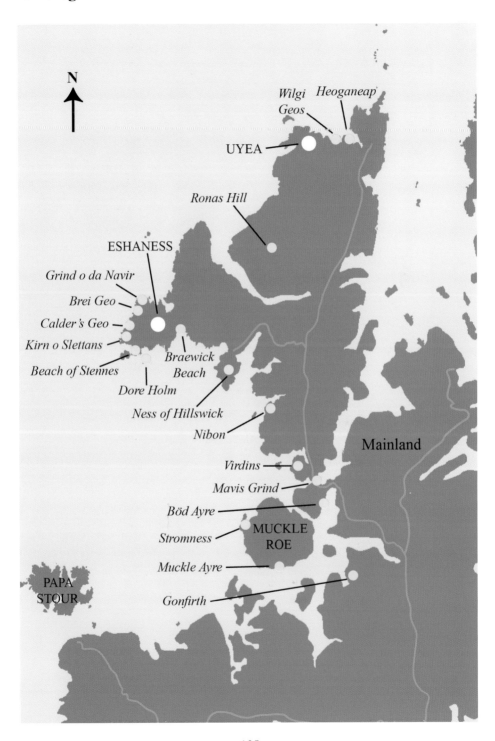

N

Wilgi Geos

Heoganeap

UYEA

Ronas Hill

ESHANESS

Grind o da Navir

Brei Geo

Calder's Geo

Kirn o Slettans

Beach of Stennes

Braewick Beach

Dore Holm

Ness of Hillswick

Nibon

Mainland

Virdins

Mavis Grind

Böd Ayre

Stromness

MUCKLE ROE

Muckle Ayre

PAPA STOUR

Gonfirth

Geological Sites and Places of Interest – South Mainland

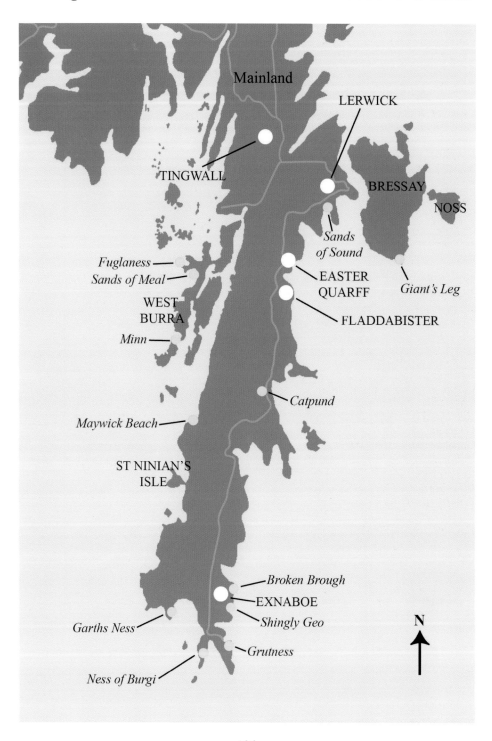

Index

About the Authors

David Malcolm was born and brought up in Fife. He and his wife Priscilla came to Shetland in 1983 where David was a partner in the Scalloway Medical Practice until he retired in 2010. Over the years he has enjoyed giving illustrated talks on natural history to many groups throughout the islands, considering himself to be a 'Jack of all trades and master of none'! He is author of A *Photographic Guide to Shetland's Wild Flowers*, the third edition of which was published by The Shetland Times in 2012.

Robina R. Barton was born in Sunderland and grew up in North Yorkshire. She has family connections in Shetland and moved to the islands in 2006, where she lives in Bressay with her husband Stuart. In 2008 she became the Geology Project Officer at Shetland Amenity Trust, responsible for coordinating the activities of Geopark Shetland. This role involves interpretation, education, promotion and conservation. Robina is a member of the European Geoparks Network Coordination Committee and the UK Geoparks Forum. In 2013 she became Chair of the Scottish Geoparks Partnership.

A proportion of the royalties arising from
the sale of this book will be donated to Geopark Shetland.

ROCKS AND MINERALS IDENTIFICATION CHART

ITEM	LOCALITY	DATE

ROCKS AND MINERALS IDENTIFICATION CHART

ITEM	LOCALITY	DATE

ROCKS AND MINERALS IDENTIFICATION CHART

ITEM	LOCALITY	DATE

ROCKS AND MINERALS IDENTIFICATION CHART

ITEM	LOCALITY	DATE

ROCKS AND MINERALS IDENTIFICATION CHART

ITEM	LOCALITY	DATE

ROCKS AND MINERALS IDENTIFICATION CHART

ITEM	LOCALITY	DATE

ROCKS AND MINERALS IDENTIFICATION CHART

ITEM	LOCALITY	DATE

ROCKS AND MINERALS IDENTIFICATION CHART

ITEM	LOCALITY	DATE

ROCKS AND MINERALS IDENTIFICATION CHART

ITEM	LOCALITY	DATE